travel
games

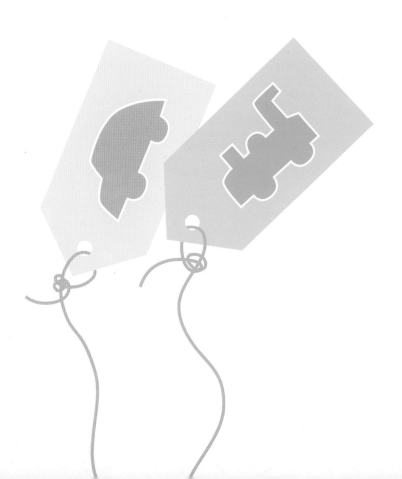

travel
games

Jane Kemp and Clare Walters
hamlyn

First published in Great Britain
in 2003 by Hamlyn, a division of
Octopus Publishing Group Ltd
2–4 Heron Quays, London E14 4JP

Copyright © Octopus Publishing
Group Ltd 2003

ISBN 0 600 60690 2

A CIP catalogue record for this book
is available from the British Library

Printed and bound in China

10 9 8 7 6 5 4 3 2 1

contents

INTRODUCTION

how to use this book

Children get bored on long journeys, and it's not always easy to get inspired about how to keep them amused when the tensions are mounting and the squabbles starting. In this book, you'll find 150 games and activities for children of all ages, ranging from simple spotting and guessing games to card games that need concentration and very silly sing-songs.

Each game or activity has lists of required items and the means of transport for which it might be appropriate, e.g. some of the pencil and paper activities would not be possible in a car and some of the noisier sing-songs might irritate other passengers on a long-haul flight or crowded train.

Every game and activity has an indication of the rough age for which it is suitable, but younger children may be able to manage a game for older children. Alternatively an older child might simply enjoy playing one suggested for a younger age group. Not every game has to be a challenge. The rules of many of the games can be adapted to take account of differing abilities, giving the younger ones a head start if you are travelling with children of different ages. Each game also has a play tip, which will help you to get the maximum enjoyment from it or give you ideas for adapting it, and each chapter has suggestions and tips on how to make the most of the type of game covered.

Mark a selection of games you think your child will enjoy before you set off, so it's easy for you to find the right ones when you're on the move, and make sure that you've got all the bits and pieces needed to hand.

Organizing all the things you need to take with you on holiday can be hectic, so the first chapter gives suggestions for what you might need to take when going on day-trips, overnight stays and longer trips. This section also contains practical advice, such as booking train seats in advance so that you can all sit together or asking for bulkhead seats on an aeroplane if you have a baby in a travel seat or carry cot.

Whether your trip is a short one to the shops or a long-haul holiday flight, you'll find lots in this book to entertain your children. Enjoy your journey!

a successful trip

Travelling with children can be reasonably stress-free as long as you anticipate your family's needs and make sure you're well prepared for the trip. No one really expects the journey to be the best part of a holiday, but with enough food, rest, toilet breaks and entertainment, it certainly doesn't have to be something to dread.

what to pack

All the basic items that you need for a journey, and for a holiday, are set out in this chapter. In addition, put a soft blanket and a pillow or two in the car to keep children comfortable when napping (but not for children under 2). It's also worth thinking about where they can keep their belongings while you're travelling. Long-handled shopping bags hung over the back of your seat or a cardboard shoe box on the back seat make good instant storage solutions.

Sleepy?
Many road accidents are caused by tired drivers desperate to get home. There's one golden rule – you MUST stop if you're tired. Even a few minutes walking up and down in a service station car park will help. Other things to try include: getting a passenger to talk to you; listening to a talk radio show; and having a caffeinated drink, such as coffee or cola.

Safe surfaces
Try a clipboard for back-seat artwork or paper games in the car. Clip the paper securely to the board to give your children a firm surface to work on.

shorter journeys

Make sure you pack a basic travel bag that's easily accessible at all times – as hand luggage on a plane or coach, or on the luggage rack in a train. Estimate the length of your journey and then double it to judge how much food to take for your children and how many changes of clothes to take for your baby.

overnight stays

Although they're the smallest travellers, babies and toddlers usually have the most luggage. Before you go, make a checklist of all the things you're likely to need. Think through 24 hours of your baby's life and write down all the things you use in that time. Then decide whether it's worth buying travel versions of these essentials, or check whether they'll be available at your destination. As a general rule, try to keep the car interior as clutter free as possible, as your children will stay much more comfortable if they've got plenty of leg room to move around.

for babies

- a travel cot and bedding
- a lightweight buggy and sunshade
- a sunproof baby tent for the beach
- baby carrier
- a portable fabric highchair
- inflatable baby bath
- sets of bottles, bottle brush, sterilizing equipment and your baby's usual milk, as well as food and cutlery if your baby is weaned
- changing bag, nappies and baby wipes (you're likely to be able to buy nappies at your destination so just take enough to get you there)
- dummies, if you use them
- sun hat, sunglasses, sun cream and UV-protective clothing
- baby moisturizing cream
- kitchen paper and supply of plastic bags
- breastpads if breastfeeding
- a few favourite toys or cuddlies
- lightweight buggy and sunshade
- sweets to suck on the plane
- comfortable clothes

for toddlers

- favourite beakers
- cups and bowls
- travel cutlery in its own case
- bibs
- potty
- walking reins
- a few favourite toys or cuddlies

for older children

- comfortable, practical clothes
- favourite toys
- travel-sized versions of popular board games
- electronic game (and spare battery)
- personal stereos (see Chapter 10)
- books, including puzzle books
- cycle helmet if you plan to cycle once you reach your destination

Plane pressure
The change in air pressure at take off and landing can cause pain in your child's ears which is relieved by swallowing. Offer your baby a feed or your toddler a chewy snack to avoid problems.

food and drink

An absolute essential on any journey – nothing raises the spirits like a tasty snack or drink. Some foods suit travelling much better than others. While there's definitely a place for crisps, chocolate and biscuits, make sure you also offer your child some healthier foods, as too much salt and sugar can make you dehydrated and irritable.
Think about: mini sandwiches, breadsticks, vegetable sticks, fresh bread, fresh fruit (crisp apples, easy-peel satsumas and firm pears). Choose small bananas and offer them first as they get squashed quickly.

Take plenty of still water on any journey, though it's also useful to have cartons of fruit juice with straws; flavoured waters for children who won't readily drink plain, and a flask of tea or coffee for the adults. Choose a spillproof beaker for your toddler, and sports bottles for older children.

Allow a bottle for every three hours if you're bottlefeeding (and cooled boiled water) and plenty of drinks for yourself if breastfeeding.

Emergency supplies
When all else fails, have an emergency supply of sweets to bring out to calm things down and generally raise morale.

All-purpose tissues
Don't forget to pack a box of tissues
for the car and a couple of packs of
travel tissues. They're not only useful
for runny noses, but also for sticky
fingers, messy faces – and when
there's no toilet paper!

travel sickness

This can affect adults and
children alike, and may make
a journey very uncomfortable.
Try to prevent it before the
journey starts by wearing travel
wristbands, or taking a suitable
medication recommended by
your pharmacist. Double-check
the age range it's suitable for,
and how long before your
journey you're meant to take it.
Feed your children an hour
before travelling to help settle
their stomachs, but avoid any
greasy or large meals. If possible
make sure there's plenty of fresh
air, and that your children don't
get overheated. Allow plenty of
time for the journey as this helps
to keep the atmosphere calm.

A child who's feeling sick may
be more comfortable in the front
of the car, or lying down if you're
on a ferry. If you can, stop the car
and have a short walk outside.
Iced water can relieve discomfort,
as can dry biscuits, anything
containing ginger, and a fresh
apple. However if the worst
happens, be prepared with a
plastic bag, a bottle of water
for rinsing and a pack of wipes.
Being able to freshen up after
a bout of sickness will really help
your child's morale.

On any journey, encourage
your children to look ahead
rather than out of side windows,
and discourage reading or
writing if you know any of them
has a tendency to travel sickness.

safety concerns

Here are some key safety points to bear in mind before you set off on your journey:

- Before starting any journey, make sure your child's car seat is fitted properly and adjusted to allow for your child's clothing. If you're hiring a car abroad, check that it will have a car seat supplied. Remember that older children also need booster seats.

- Don't put your baby's car seat in the front if your car is fitted with airbags. These are extremely dangerous for children if they inflate. Secure it in the back and buy a rear-view baby mirror.

- Be especially careful with hot drinks on trains: the swaying motion of the train can easily tip them over.

- Never leave children unattended in the car, even for a short time. Accidents can happen in moments, and it's just not worth the risk. In some countries, it is illegal, anyway.

- Never allow children to fiddle with the controls in the car. Electric windows and sun roofs are potentially extremely dangerous, so make sure your child is not able to operate them by making sure that the car seatbelt is securely fastened.

- On a boat trip, keep your children close at all times as it would be all to easy for them to slip through barriers or railings.

- Make sure you have a fully charged mobile phone with you for any emergencies. If you belong to a rescue service, make sure your membership is up to date and you have your card with you. Before you go abroad, make sure that your phone will work there.

- When driving, resist the temptation to turn around to try to sort out squabbles. Doing this, even for a few seconds, could cause an accident.

first aid kit

Before you go, make sure your first aid box is up to date. There are lots of travel-sized kits available from any chemist but if you want to make up a basic one of your own it should contain:

- Sticking plasters
- Antiseptic cream or wipes
- Several clean non-fluffy dressings
- Adhesive tape
- Infant paracetamol
- Rehydrating sachets
- Pain relief spray for bites and stings
- Cotton wool
- Themometer
- Calamine lotion
- Tweezers
- Scissors
- Gauze bandage
- Triangular bandage
- Safety pins

If your kit contains any pills or medicines, make sure it is secured in a locked glove compartment away from your children. Be sure you have enough supplies of any prescribed medicines for you or your child and don't leave packs of pills in a bag where a toddler could discover them. An empty box or plastic bag is also useful in case your child feels sick.

Baby seatbelt
On a plane, if you haven't been given a baby seat belt, ask the cabin attendant to supply you with one that can be clipped to your own seat belt.

Spray cool
Travelling can make your skin feel dry – a water spray will give you an instant lift. Buy a can or make your own with a small plastic spray bottle.

sun care

If you're travelling in the summer, you'll no doubt hope to enjoy some sunshine. Bear in mind the key tips on the right for staying safe in the sun to be sure of getting the most out of your holiday.

top tips

- **Wear a hat**
  To avoid overheating and sunstroke your baby must wear a hat. Look for a wide-brimmed hat with a flap to protect your baby's neck. Babies often pull their hats off but you'll need to be firm about keeping it on. Encourage your toddler by wearing a hat yourself.

- **Stay in the shade**
  It's essential for babies under the age of one to be kept out of the sun at all times. Even older children should avoid the sun between 11am and 3pm, when it's at its hottest. This applies when you're walking around – not just at the beach. A pram hood could cause overheating as it restricts ventilation, so use a sunshade or parasol, or invest in a UV sun protection buggy cover. This allows air through but protects your child from the sun.

• **Use suncream**
Cover all exposed skin
whenever you're out and
about. Reapply every hour or
more often if your child is
playing in water, and leave a
visible film. Don't forget ears,
nose and feet. Children's skin is
much more sensitive than
adults', and any sunburn could
increase their risk of
developing skin cancer later in
life. Use a sun cream with a
high protection factor (at least
SPF25, or more if you're in a
really hot climate, and
preferably a sun block). UV
protective clothing is a great
way to keep kids safe while
they're playing on the beach.

• **Wear sensible clothing**
Cover shoulders with a loosely
fitting close-weave T-shirt, or
UV protective suit. Choose long
sleeved or elbow length tops
and surf-style shorts that cover
more of your child's legs. Some
children's sunglasses have
stretchy bands to hold them in
place – great for busy toddlers.

• **Drink plenty of water**
Easy to forget, but absolutely
essential especially when
you're spending a lot of time
outdoors. Give your child
frequent drinks and don't wait
for them to ask. Plain water,
or well diluted juices are ideal –
carry a large bottleful at all
times.

2

spotting games

GETTING IT RIGHT

Spotting games are always useful because they need very few props and you can make them as long or short as you wish. To really enjoy a spotting game, follow the tips below:

- If your children are feeling sick, don't encourage them to look out of the side windows of a car – it will only make them feel worse.

- Make all the rules clear before you begin.

- Be realistic about the sort of objects you're likely to see in the area that you are currently travelling through (i.e. few shops will be visible from a motorway)

- Be fair – older children will have the advantage in these games, so allow younger ones extra time or a bit of help.

spotting list

age 5+
you'll need pencils and paper
suitable for car, train, boat

An easy spotting game. Make a list of ten things you're likely to see on your journey. Your children have to look out for them and tick them off as they spot them. For example, on a boat trip you could suggest a seagull, a steward in uniform, a deck chair, etc.

Play tip
If any of your children are not yet able to read, draw the items for them to spot instead.

- Intersperse spotting games with some other sorts of games, as they can be tiring on the eyes.

spot a shop

age 5+
you'll need pencils and paper
suitable for car, train

Make a list for each child of five objects that you would buy in specific shops. Then give each child their list and ask them to tick off the items as they see the correct shops. A sample list might be: a pair of shoes (shoe shop); a bag of apples (greengrocer's); stamps (post office); a packet of plasters (chemist); and a book (bookshop). If two people are looking for the same shop and see it at the same time, the person who shouts its name first gets it. The first to tick off all the items on their list is the winner.

Play tip
A huge variety of things can be bought at supermarkets, so decide before the game starts whether you are going to allow them or not.

spot the dot

age 3+
you'll need A packet of small stick-on dots
suitable for car, boat, train, plane

Ask your child to hide his eyes while you stick a small dot somewhere nearby, such as on the car dashboard. Then tell him to open his eyes and see if he can spot the dot. Obviously the younger the child, the clearer the hiding place needs to be.

Play tip
If you're playing this game in the car, make sure that the dot can be seen from your child's viewpoint, so that he doesn't need to wriggle too much in his car seat.

what country?

age 5+
you'll need nothing
suitable for car

Ask your children to look out for cars with stickers or licence plates that identify which country or state they're from. They get one point for every different one they spot and another if they can also name the country or state.

Play tip
You could play this game where a third point is awarded for any extra information your children can supply about the country or state.

red car

age 3+
you'll need nothing
suitable for car, train

This is the simplest of all spotting games. Set a time limit and get the children to guess how many red cars you think you will pass in that time. Then count how many do and see whose guess was closest. If you're on the train, substitute horses, fields of cattle, telegraph posts or churches for red cars.

Play tip
Alternatively, each child could choose a favourite colour car to spot.

road signs

age 4+
you'll need nothing
suitable for car

See how many road signs you can spot, and ask your children if they can identify what they mean. Can they also see a variety of different shapes signs, e.g. circular, square, rectangular or diamond-shaped?

Play tip
To make it more fun, they could think of alternative meanings for the signs.

I spy

age 4+
you'll need nothing
suitable for car, train, boat, plane

You'll almost certainly remember this classic game from your own childhood. You begin the game by thinking of an object you can see and saying, 'I spy with my little eye something beginning with "D".' The others have to say all the words they can think of beginning with 'D' until they hit on the right one. (Use phonetic sounds if you prefer.)

Play tip
For younger children either specify what sort of thing you spied, e.g. an animal beginning with 'C' (a cow), or play it with colours instead of letters, e.g. 'I spy with my little eye something that is green' (the grass).

Coach stops
If you're travelling by coach, ask if it has a toilet as you won't be able to stop when you want to. If there isn't a toilet, take your children to the toilet before the journey.

find the colours
age 2+
you'll need nothing
suitable for car, boat, train, plane

Choose a colour that you know your child knows (his favourite colour is a good starting point), then simply ask him to name as many objects as he can see of that colour.

Play tip
If you feel there isn't enough to see of any one colour, ask your child to think of as many things of that colour instead.

lucky numbers
age 5+
you'll need nothing
suitable for car

Each child chooses a number from zero to nine as a 'lucky number', and then has to look out for it on the number plates of parked cars, winning a point for each one.

Play tip
If this is too easy, give your children two numbers each that have to be found together.

count up
age 6+
you'll need pencil and paper
suitable for car, train, boat

Give points to all the things you're likely to see on your journey, and ask your child to keep a tally of these as she spots them. You could allocate points to each thing, so you can add up how many points each player has scored at the end of the game. Examples might be: one point for every motorbike or tractor; two points for every ladder or crane; three points for every person wearing a hat or carrying a suitcase.

Play tip
Set a time limit to avoid the points system of this game becoming too complicated.

who's first to see...

age 3+
you'll need nothing
suitable for car, train, boat, plane

You spot something and ask the children who can see it too – rather like I Spy but without the guessing. For example, you could say, 'Who's first to see ... the boy with the stripey jumper?' or '... the suitcase with the red strap?'

Play tip
The first one to see the item can then choose the next thing for everyone to spot.

rainbow road

age 3+
you'll need nothing
suitable for car

Look for cars that are the colours of the rainbow, and try to spot them in the right order so that you make up your own rainbow road. The colours are red, orange, yellow, green, blue, indigo and violet.

Play tip
You could make this easier by creating your own 'rainbow' of car colours, such as silver, black and white, that you're more likely to see on the road.

alphabet picture

age 5+
you'll need A colourful picture book, or a full-page picture torn out of a magazine
suitable for car, boat, train, plane

This simple version of *I Spy* is picture-based. Get your children to look at a large picture and, going through the alphabet, see if they can find an object beginning with each letter. Get older children to see if they can spot more than one object for each letter.

Play tip
To really enjoy this game, it's best to have a very lively busy picture with lots of detail.

sound spotting

age 4+
you'll need nothing
suitable for car, boat, train, plane

Ask your children to close their eyes and 'spot' sounds they hear around them. These might include a car horn, a dog barking, a baby crying, a police siren, a plane going overhead, the sound of the engine, the call of birds like gulls, the radio, and so on. This game is best played in a reasonably quiet environment, such as when the car is in a quiet road or a traffic jam.

Play tip

Imagine you're at the coast and think of all the sounds you might hear there. Other ideas are in a wood, in the garden, by a river, near a school and on a building site.

Train tip

When booking ahead for a train journey, ask if you can have seats near the buffet to make getting drinks and snacks quicker and easier.

where are the rabbits?

age 2+
you'll need a few detailed pictures torn out from magazines and a pencil or felt pen
suitable for boat, train, plane

This is an easy, but popular, idea that you see in lots of children's comics. Simply draw six little 'hidden' objects in the picture for your child to find. Good objects include:
- rabbits
- ice-cream cones
- stars
- hearts
- arrows
- hats

Play tip

Toddlers may find this hard so hide the objects in obvious places. For older children you can be much more subtle – make the objects smaller and hide them in more obscure parts of the picture.

who's wearing a red t-shirt?

age 2+
you'll need nothing
suitable for car, boat, train, plane

This game is ideal for tinies. Just choose something someone on the journey with you is wearing and ask your child if she can spot who it is. Vary your questions according to the age of the children playing the game. For example, you could ask a young child something obvious, such as, 'Who in this car is wearing a blue jumper?' or an older one something more subtle, like, 'Who in our family is wearing a digital watch?'

Play tip
Vary the game by suggesting two things to look for, e.g. 'Who is wearing white shoelaces and gold earrings?'

how many stars?

age 3+
you'll need paper and pencil
suitable for boat, train, plane

This one is easy yet fun. Just draw a sky full of stars (or clouds, birds, planets, or planes) and ask a young child to count how many she can see. If your child is older, show her the picture for a moment and then ask her to guess how many she thinks there are. Once your child has counted the stars, she can add some more of her own and ask you to guess how many there are altogether now.

Play tip
Match the number of stars to your child's counting ability – so she always feels that she has succeeded at the game.

CHAPTER 3

musical
games

GETTING IT RIGHT

There's nothing like a sing-song in the car to pass the miles, and a rousing song can also be a good way to distract children who are starting to squabble with each other. Here are a few good ideas:

- Musical games and songs are great fun to sing together, but do bear in mind that other travellers in a coach, train or plane may find it irritating to have a family sing-song going on nearby. And you may also find your children become too self-conscious to join in properly in any case.

- If you're travelling with a group of children, choose songs where the verse doesn't change significantly. This makes it much easier for everyone to join in quickly, even if they don't know the song to start with. *Ten Green Bottles* and *One Man Went to Mow* are good examples.

- Don't worry about the quality of your singing – it's having fun and passing the time that are important.

- Make sure you have a good stock of music or story tapes in the car to keep the children amused when you don't feel like singing any more or need to concentrate on driving.

- Ask your children for song ideas too – there may be a great song they've learned at nursery or school that they'll enjoy teaching you.

- When children are old enough – from around four – you may want to let them have their own cassette player with headphones so they can listen to what they want.

ABC alphabet song

age 4+
you'll need nothing
suitable for car

Sing the letters of the alphabet through from A to Z to the tune of *Twinkle, Twinkle, Little Star*. Break it up like this:

A, B, C, D, E, F, G
H, I, J, K, L, M, N, O, P
Q, R, S, T, U, V,
W, X, Y, Z
(now back to the beginning of the tune)
Now you know your A, B, C,
Won't you sing along with me!

Play tip
You might have to go through the 'L, M, N, O, P' slowly at first so little ones don't think of them as all one letter!

Better in the back
When you're playing travel games it's best if one adult sits in the back with the children – you may not have as much leg room but it saves you having to keep leaning round from the front seat. The younger the children, the more they'll need you close at hand to supervise any games or songs. You may also find it helps to sit between children you know are going to squabble.

one, two, buckle my shoe

age 3+
you'll need nothing
suitable for car, boat, train

This classic rhyme involves lots of fun actions, such as flapping your arms like the hen's wings, or digging with a pretend spade:

One, two, buckle my shoe,
Three, four, knock at the door.
Five, six, pick up sticks,
Seven, eight, lay them straight.
Nine, ten, a big fat hen,
Eleven, twelve, dig and delve.
Thirteen, fourteen,
Maids a courting.
Fifteen, sixteen,
Maids in the kitchen.
Seventeen, eighteen,
Maids in waiting.
Nineteen, twenty,
My plate's empty!

Play tip
For younger children, stop the rhyme when you get to ten or twelve. If they're enjoying it you can repeat the rhyme from the beginning.

Drive time
The type of music you play in the car can affect the way you drive. Don't play lullabies if you are feeling sleepy.

ten green bottles
age 3+
you'll need nothing
suitable for car

This well-known song is a great game for helping children learn about counting down from ten to one – it's also so easy that even very young ones can join in.

Ten green bottles
standing on the wall.
Ten green bottles
standing on the wall.
And if one green bottle
should accidentally fall,
There'd be nine green bottles
standing on the wall.

Play tip
Hold up ten fingers to start the song and fold one down as each bottle falls off the wall.

one man went to mow
age 3+
you'll need
suitable for car

This rousing number is great for long journeys as it lasts a good long time and also helps with counting practice. The countdown from ten men can end with a dramatic slowed down – and loud – last line.

One man went to mow,
went to mow a meadow.
One man and his dog,
went to mow a meadow.

Two men went to mow,
went to mow a meadow,
Two men, one man
and his dog,
went to mow a meadow.

Three men ...etc

Play tip
Add a different 'woof woof' after the dog gets mentioned in each verse.

Incy Wincy spider

age 2+
you'll need nothing
suitable for car, boat, train, plane

A classic game that children love.
There are lots of simple actions to
enjoy, too. Starting in your lap,
put your hands across each other
so the thumb of one hand
touches the little finger of the
other hand. 'Walk' Incy up the
spout by turning one hand over
the other. For the rain, sprinkle
your fingers downwards to make
'raindrops'. Spread your fingers
to make a sun; then repeat the
climbing motion for the final
line.

Incy Wincy Spider,
climbing up the spout
Down came the rain and
washed poor Incy out.
Out came the sunshine and
dried up all the rain,
Incy Wincy spider
climbed up the spout again!

Play tip
If your child is sitting in you lap on a
boat, train or plane, you could simply
'walk' your fingers up their arm to
be Incy. Then they can have a turn to
make their fingers into Incy walking
up your arm or back.

hum that tune

age 5+
you'll need nothing
suitable for car, train, boat

Think of a tune your child knows
well. Hum the first few notes and
ask if he can guess what tune it
is. Gradually increase the number
of notes you sing until he guesses
correctly. Good songs to try
include nursery rhymes
(*Lavender's Blue, Ring-a-Ring-o-*
Roses), well-known tunes (*Yellow*
Submarine) and, for older
children, familiar pop songs.

Play tip
If your child guesses correctly it's fun
to sing the tune through together.

sing a note each

age 4+
you'll need nothing
suitable for car

Pick a simple song or nursery
rhyme. Going round in turn, sing
consecutive notes so that you are
singing the song one note at a
time.

Play tip
Make sure you pick a tune that
everyone knows really well, such as
***Happy Birthday* or *Rock a Bye Baby*.**

ROUNDS

Rounds are generally suitable for older children, although younger ones might enjoy trying to join in. To sing a round you need one person to start the first line; then the next person begins the song when the first person reaches the second line. Continue in this way for up to four people.

Frère Jacques

age 5+
you'll need nothing
suitable for car

An ever-popular round that incorporates a handy bit of French practice too.

Frère Jacques, Frère Jacques
Dormez-vous? Dormez-vous?
Sonnez les matines,
sonnez les matines,
Ding dang dong,
ding dang dong.

Play tip

If the French version is too much you could replace it with English words: Brother John, are you sleeping, morning bells are ringing, ding, dong, ding.

I hear thunder

age 4+
you'll need Nothing
suitable for car

Sing this song to the tune of Frère Jacques with some simple actions. Cup your hand behind your ears for 'I hear thunder' and 'Hark don't you'; make 'raindrops' with your fingers; and shiver for being 'wet through'.

I hear thunder, I hear thunder.
Hark, don't you?
Hark, don't you?
Pitter patter raindrops,
pitter patter raindrops.
I'm wet through, so are you!

Play tip

If your child is finding it hard to hold the tune on his own, let him team up with an adult for their part of the round.

kookaburra

age 4+
you'll need Nothing
suitable for car

This is another favourite round about an Australian bird with a distinctive laughing call.

> Kookaburra sits in the old gum tree,
> Merry, merry king of the bush is he,
> Laugh, Kookaburra, laugh,
> Kookaburra, gay your life must be.

Play tip

This might give you the chance to talk to your child about other well-known bird sounds, such as the cuckoo, a dove's cooing or a duck quacking.

Stay fresh

Keep fresh air circulating in the car by opening the roof or taking turns to have your window open. Leaving the heater on without some fresh air can leave you all feeling heavy-headed.

London's burning

age 4+
you'll need Nothing
suitable for car

> London's burning,
> London's burning.
> Fetch the engines,
> Fetch the engines.
> Fire, fire! Fire, fire!
> Pour on water, pour on water.
> Fire, fire! Fire, fire!

Play tip

Help older children to make up words to this tune once they know it well enough. It's fun if these relate to your family, for example:

> Tom was hungry,
> Tom was hungry,
> Ate a sandwich,
> Ate a sandwich,
> Peanut butter,
> Peanut butter,
> Yum, yum! Yum, yum!

mind the gap!

age 3+
you'll need nothing
suitable for car

Pick a song that your children know the words to, and sing it, leaving a pause at the end of each line so that they can fill in the missing word. For example, if you start off, 'Lavender's Blue, dilly dilly, Lavender's...' your children finish with 'Green'.

Play tip
You could adapt this as a 'spot what's wrong in the song' game, singing, for example , 'Humpty Dumpty Sat on a Chair' or 'Jack and Jill went up the mountain', to see if your children can spot the wrong word.

Tray play
A small tray with a lip all around the edge is a really practical way of helping older children play with little bricks, paper dolls or pen and paper games.

one finger, one thumb

age 3+
you'll need nothing
suitable for car

The song below builds up to a fun wriggling and shaking end. Sing it as loudly as you like, adding the appropriate actions, to put everyone in a really good mood.

One finger, one thumb keep moving.
One finger, one thumb keep moving.
One finger, one thumb keep moving,
We'll all be merry and bright.

One finger, one thumb, one arm keep moving...

One finger, one thumb, one arm, one leg keep moving...

One finger, one thumb, one arm, one leg, one head keep moving...

Play tip
You can add extra verses if you want to keep the game going for longer. Try 'elbow', 'knee' and 'foot'.

name the instruments

age 6+
you'll need a pre-prepared cassette or CD with a variety of music, or a selection of CDs or tapes and a CD- or cassette-player
suitable for car, or boat, train or plane using headphones.

Enjoy listening to a piece of music that features one particular instrument, such as a guitar, piano, or violin then ask your children if they can guess which instrument they've just heard.

Play tip
To make this harder, choose a piece that features several instruments and see how many they can identify.

fast and slow songs

age 4+
you'll need nothing
suitable for car

Choose a song that every one in your family knows well, but don't let on what it is. Then sing it at top speed to see if your children can identify it. Alternatively, try singing it as slowly as you can.

Play tip
You could also try singing songs in a very high or very low voice.

if you're happy and you know it

age 2+
you'll need nothing
suitable for car

This fun family song can keep them busy for as long as you want. Sing the verses, doing the actions as you go:

If you're happy and you know it clap your hands. (clap, clap)
If you're happy and you know it clap your hands. (clap, clap)
If you're happy and you know it,
And you really want to show it,
If you're happy and you know it clap your hands. (clap, clap).

Subsequent verses could include actions like:
● stamp your feet
● nod your head
● tap your nose
● shout 'We are!'

Play tip
Ask your child to think of some actions that you could all do – the sillier the better.

guessing games

GETTING IT RIGHT

Guessing games can be really easy travel games to play, but at the same time they'll engage your children's curiosity and exercise their powers of deduction.

- You'll use your voice a lot for these games, so they're best played in a relatively quiet place so you don't have to shout to be heard.

- Encourage your children to take turns at being the quiz master from time to time rather than always leading the game yourself.

- If you need a dice, you might find one in a popular travel game, like Ludo or Snakes and Ladders, or you could make your own from a cardboard hexagon with a used matchstick stuck through the middle. Alternatively, buy a packet from a toy shop.

odd one out
age 4+
you'll need nothing
suitable for car, train, boat, plane

Say a list of things out loud that are all connected in some way, for example, animals or food items. Casually drop in a word that is entirely unrelated, and see if your child notices. If she does, she gets the next turn.

Play tip
You could make the odd one out quite subtle for older children, for example 'cat, dog, mouse, person' is easy, but 'tiger, lion, panther, elephant' is harder.

- At the start of a car journey, ask everyone to guess how many miles the trip will be. Offer a prize at the end to the person who gets the nearest guess. Check the milometer at the beginning and end of the trip.

- Even babies and very young children will enjoy simple guessing games, such as *Peek-a-boo* or *Hide the Toy* (where you half hide a toy under your coat).

roll the dice

age 4+
you'll need dice
suitable for train, boat, plane

Everyone chooses a number
between one and six and you roll
the die to see if whose number
comes up. That person then gets
the next go at rolling the die.

Play tip
For older children use two dice; the
winner is the person whose number
is nearest.

where in the world am I?

age 5+
you'll need nothing
suitable for car, train, boat, plane

Think of a place and describe it
to your children. Ask them to
guess where you are from your
description. It could be a country,
a town, a building or even the
holiday resort where you last
stayed. For example, 'I'm
standing in front of a tall metal
tower in a busy city. Everyone
around me is speaking French.
Where in the world am I?'

Play tip
For younger children, pretend you're
in a particular room in the house and
describe what it's like.

code

age 6+
you'll need pencil and paper
suitable for car, train, boat, plane

Write out the letters of the
alphabet and put numbers
underneath each letter (so A is 1,
B is 2, C is 3 and so on). Then
write a short message using the
appropriate numbers instead of
the letters. Ask the children to
unscramble the code to read your
message.

Play tip
Another code to try could be where
you move the letters on one, so A
becomes B and so on. Alternatively,
your children may like to make up
their own secret code symbols.

what's your job?
age 3+
you'll need nothing
suitable for car, train, boat, plane

One person decides what job they do and the others have to guess what it is by asking questions. For instance the job might be a fire-fighter and the questions could be such things as:
- 'Do you work in an office?'
- 'Would we see you in a shop?'
- 'Do you make things?'

Play tip
Make sure the job you choose will be something the younger members of the family will recognize.

number story
age 5+
you'll need nothing
suitable for car, boat, train, plane

Make up a simple story that features two children and a variety of situations involving numbers. Each time you come to one of these, ask your children to help you do the sum. For example, 'Once upon a time there were two children called Sam and Lizzie. One day their mum made them a picnic with eight sandwiches in it. How many did they have each? Then they picked the same number of apples from the tree. They picked 20 apples! How many did each of them pick?' and so on.

Play tip
If your child can manage these easily, try harder divisions like three or four.

Avoid the crowds
When travelling with children on trains, avoid the rush hour, if possible, as it will be less crowded and you're likely to get seats.

three of a kind

age 3+
you'll need nothing
suitable for car, boat, train, plane

Choose a category and ask your
children to think of three things
that would fit into it, e.g.
- three kinds of sandwich filling
- three kinds of dog
- three kinds of house

Play tip
Make the game harder for older
children: ask them to add words to a
'base' word, e.g. 'wood': woodland,
woodpecker and firewood.

I'm famous!

age 6+
you'll need nothing
suitable for car, train, boat, plane

Think of a famous person or
book or television character that
your children will know, such as
Winnie-the-Pooh. Then say, 'I am
a little, friendly bear who loves
sweet things'. The other players
have to ask questions with yes or
no answers, such as:
- 'Do you like marmalade?' (No)
- 'Do you like honey?' (Yes)
- 'Are you Winnie-the-Pooh?'
  (Yes, I am)

Play tip
Help struggling children with some
leading questions.

guess what I'm doing

age 4+
you'll need nothing
suitable for car, train, boat, plane

Think of an everyday action such
as making a cup of tea, going out
for a walk or paying for milk in
the shop. You have to act out the
scene using only sounds and
actions, but no words at all. The
others have to guess what you're
doing as accurately as possible.
The first to guess correctly has
the next turn.

Play tip
Keep this game easier for young
children by simply making animal
sounds and asking them to guess
which animal you are. Then they can
have a turn at making a noise for
you to guess.

who lives here?

age 2+
you'll need nothing
suitable for car, boat, train, plane

Start the game by describing a particular sort of animal house, then ask your child if she can think who might live in it. You could try, 'The animal house I am thinking of is quite big, has lots of straw on the floor and some hay to eat. It also has a special door that divides in two so that the animal can look outside.' Your child might say 'Horse' immediately, but if not you can add some more obvious clues, such as, 'You might find a saddle or reins in here,' or 'It's called a stable,' to help her.

Play tip
This game can be made more fun – and more noisy – by making the animal sounds once the animal has been guessed correctly.

who wears the flippers?

Age 3+
You'll need nothing
Suitable for car, boat, train, plane

Many occupations require specific clothing. In this game, you describe a particular item, such as a pair of flippers, then list a number of options for who might wear them. For example, 'I'm wearing a pair of flippers. Am I a doctor, firefighter, ballet dancer, teacher, diver or cleaner?'

Play tip
Once one child has guessed, see if she can identify the other clothes and equipment that person would need to do their job, for example a mask, wetsuit, snorkel, etc.

where's it gone?

age 2+
you'll need a small object and three plastic or polystyrene cups
suitable for train, boat, plane

Upturn the cups and hide the object under one of them. Then shuffle the cups around and ask your children to guess which cup the toy is hidden under.

Play tip
Speed up the shuffling for older children or ask them to try catching you out.

heads or tails?

age 3+
you'll need a coin
suitable for car, train, boat, plane

A game that's a handy time-filler if you're delayed or kept waiting unexpectedly. Simply toss a coin in the air and cover it. Your child has to guess whether it's heads or tails.

Play tip
Play this as the best of five, seven or nine.

guess the fairytale

age 4+
you'll need nothing
suitable for car, boat, train, plane

Describe the main characters and settings of a fairy tale, without giving away any names, e.g. 'In this fairytale, there's a little girl going to visit her grandmother, and a big, bad wolf,' and see if your children can guess which one you have in mind.

Play tip
If she still can't guess, you could add an easier clue such as, 'The girl wears a red cloak.'

who won?

age 6+
you'll need pen and paper
suitable for car, boat, train, plane

Draw three stickmen at the start of a winding 'race-track' with three separate lanes. Mark the finishing line and then draw a different number of dots along each lane for each stickman. Tell your child that each dot represents one minute and ask him if he can count up how many minutes each runner took to complete the race – and who was the winner.

Play tip
To make the game harder, use a dot to symbolize one minute, a dash for two minutes and a triangle for three minutes.

Don't wait!
Get your toddler to use the toilet in the airport before boarding a plane as you won't be able to use the plane's toilets straightaway.

20 questions

age 6+
you'll need nothing
suitable for car, train, boat, plane

The first player thinks of an object that has to be broadly classified either as an animal (e.g. pig), vegetable (e.g. daffodil) or mineral (e.g. vase). You may need to explain this difficult concept more carefully to younger children. The game opens with the other players asking whether it's animal, vegetable or mineral. They then have a further 19 questions to establish what the object is but your answers can only be 'yes' or 'no'. For example, 'Are you an animal we'd find on a farm?' When they think they know the answer they can guess, but if it's wrong, this guess counts as a question. You win if they reach 20 questions without guessing correctly.

Play tip
Take turns to choose the object, as otherwise it tends always to be the same person guessing correctly.

tops and bottoms

age 2+
You'll need nothing
Suitable for car, boat, train, plane

Pretend to be an animal, but only describe your face and your tail, e.g. 'I have pink ears, a snouty nose, and my tail is pink and curly. What am I?' Your children have to guess what sort of animal you are.

Play tip
If your child has trouble guessing, describe, one by one, other characteristics that would identify the animal, e.g. its feet or fur.

what a jumble!

age 4+
you'll need nothing
suitable for car, boat, train, plane

Think of a simple sentence, then say the words in the wrong order to your children, e.g. 'Favourite my is red colour.' See if they can work out what the correct order should be. Then let them have turns at muddling up sentences for you to solve, too.

Play tip
For older children you could play this as a written game with longer sentences.

guess the missing number

age 5+
You'll need nothing
Suitable for car, boat, train, plane

This is a game of number sequences. Start with the easiest sequence of all – counting from one to ten, leaving out one of the numbers. See if your children can say which was missing. If they're confident with this, try counting up in twos or tens, or counting backwards.

Play tip
Try easy counting, but start at 100, e.g. what's missing from 100, 101, 102, 103, 105?

big and small numbers

age 4+
You'll need nothing
Suitable for car, boat, train, plane

Say a list of random numbers out loud, then ask your child to tell you which was the biggest number you said. Then give her another list and ask for the smallest number. Vary the numbers according to your child's ability, for example, a four-year-old will cope with numbers from 1 to 10 such as 8, 3, 5 and 9.

Play tip
For older children use hundreds or even thousands for more of a challenge, or simply make the list longer.

CHAPTER 5

pencil and paper games

GETTING IT RIGHT

These are mainly suitable for older children whose pencil skills are mature enough to cope with the games. Here are some tips to keep the games running smoothly:

- Just before you set out on your journey, give each child a new notebook and pencil to keep in their backpack or bag. Even if they are too young to play many paper and pencil games they will enjoy drawing in it.

- Put a pencil sharpener in your bag, and insist that it comes straight back to you after it's been used – otherwise it will quickly disappear!

- A packet of colouring pencils or crayons are useful as your child may enjoy colouring in the pictures you've created in a game. Wax crayons may not be a good idea if you're going to a very hot country as they might soften.

boxes

age 5+
you'll need paper and pencil
suitable for train, boat, plane

Draw a grid of dots, five down and five across. Each player connects two dots in turn, either vertically or horizontally. The player who completes the fourth side of a 'box' can write her initials in the box and have another go. The person with the most boxes wins.

Play tip
To make it easier, use a smaller grid.

- Don't play a paper and pencil game in the car if any of your children are feeling travel sick as this will make them feel worse.

- These games are best played on a flat surface when you've got time to fill, such as in an airport while waiting for your flight.

- Don't give your children felt pens or ballpoint pens to carry, as they can very easily end up staining their clothes if the cap comes off.

make a man

age 4+
you'll need paper and pencil
suitable for train, boat, plane

Think of a word and draw dashes for each letter of the word. Your child has to guess one letter at a time. If the letter is in the word, it gets written on the appropriate dash. If not, you can draw the head of a man. The next time a wrong letter is chosen, you can add a body, then arms and legs, hands and feet. If you complete your man before your child has guessed the word, you win. Then swap over and let your child choose the mystery word.

Play tip
If your child's spelling is shaky, she may like to choose a word from something she can see, such as a story book.

scribble pictures

age 5+
you'll need pencil and paper
suitable for train, boat, plane

Draw a scribble on a piece of paper and hand it to your child to make a proper picture out of it. You can help by suggesting a starting point, such as, 'That looks a bit like a pair of glasses – perhaps you could make it into a funny man.' Keep the scribbles as simple shapes to start with so your child builds confidence, for example a wiggly line can easily become a snake or worm. Then it's your turn to create an artwork from her scribble!

Play tip
If your child is enjoying this she may want to colour in some of the better pictures you've created together.

add a line
age 4+
you'll need pencil and paper
suitable for train, boat, plane

Take it in turns to draw a line, and see if you can make a simple picture. You can use curved, straight or wiggly lines. For example you could start with a circle for a face, and take turns to add the features. It can be as silly or as sensible as you like!

Play tip
For younger children, tell them in advance what the drawing is going to be, such as a house or boat.

Clothes sense
To keep comfortable when travelling, dress yourself and your children in light layers so that you can easily adjust your clothing to changes in temperature and weather. Make sure everyone has comfortable shoes and socks, too.

picture consequences
age 4+
you'll need paper and pencil
suitable for train, boat, plane

Give each player a piece of paper (you may want to divide an A4 piece into two vertical strips). Ask everyone to draw a funny head and the beginning of a neck. They then fold the top of the paper down so you can just see the bottom of the neck but the rest of the picture is hidden. Everyone passes on their paper to the person on their left, who draws a funny body and arms, ending at the waist. The paper is folded over again, passed on and the next person draws the lower half of the body down to the ankles; the last person does the feet, and gives a name to the character.

Pass the papers on again, and unfold the pictures to enjoy some weird and wonderful people!

Play tip
For older children, play consequences with words, e.g. Mr xxx met Miss xxxx at a xxxx. He said xxxxx, she said xxxxx, and the consequence was xxxxxxx.

take a pencil for a walk

age 3+

you'll need pencil and paper, and crayons

suitable for train, boat, plane

Ask everyone to take their pencil for a 'walk' all over a page, criss-crossing lines to make a big, loopy pattern. They can then colour in the spaces trying to avoid getting the same colour in adjoining spaces.

Play tip
The more colours you have, the more effective your pattern will be.

what's missing?

age 3+

you'll need pencil and paper

suitable for train, boat, plane

Draw a picture of a familiar object but leave off one key element. Then ask your children to spot what's missing. Try face with only one ear, a jug without a handle, a car with three wheels or a house with no door. When one child has guessed correctly, add in the missing item.

Play tip
If your children enjoy this game, try it with two missing elements.

categories

age 6+

you'll need pencil and paper

suitable for train, boat, plane

Choose five categories and write them down the side of the page, e.g. girl's name, boy's name, food, animal or colour. Choose a starter word such as 'table' and spell it out across the top of the page. When you say 'Go!' everyone has to find a word for each category beginning with each of the letters in your word, i.e. T, A, B, L and E. The winner is the first to fill in all the categories.

Play tip
To make the game easier, choose fewer categories and a three-letter word.

noughts and crosses (tic tac toe)

age 4+

you'll need pencil and paper

suitable for train, boat, plane

A well-known game that children love. Draw two horizontal lines across two vertical lines to make a grid of nine spaces. Then choose to be either an O or an X or, if you have more than one child nominate them, and take turns to fill the spaces. The winner is the first person to complete a straight line of Os or Xs in either a vertical, horizontal or diagonal direction.

Play tip

Make a larger grid to extend the game.

what's wrong?

age 3+

you'll need pencil and paper

suitable for boat, train, plane

Draw a picture where something's obviously not right, for example a bicycle with square wheels, a fish with a moustache, an umbrella with the spokes going the wrong way, a girl wearing odd shoes, or a teapot with the spout curving downwards. Ask your child if she can spot what's wrong.

Play tip

Ask your child to think of a funny picture that has something wrong with it and draw it for her.

colour in the flags

age 3+

you'll need pencil and paper

suitable for car, boat, train, plane

Draw a string of triangular flags across sheets of paper and ask your children to make each one individual with its own colours and patterns.

Play tip

Instead of flags you could draw beads on a necklace, carriages on a train or a bunch of balloons

how many words?

age 6+
you'll need pencil and paper
suitable for train, boat, plane

Choose a fairly long word and write it across the top of your child's piece of paper. Ask her to see how many new words she can make out of it, and write these down. You can play alongside helping her, or leave her to it if she is a confident speller. Words to start with could be: SUPERMARKET, TRANSPORT, PLAYTIME or ELEPHANT.

Play tip
Two-letter words are allowed in this game.

dot to dot

age 3+
you'll need pencil and paper
suitable for train, boat, plane

Very faintly draw a large outline of a familiar object for each child. Then, more firmly, add in some dots along the outline. Give your child the pencil and let her connect the dots to complete the picture. Objects to try might include a teddy, a bus, a house or a cat.

Play tip
Add extra features to the picture once your child has finished the outline.

spot the difference

age 3+
you'll need pencil and paper
suitable for train, boat, plane

This is a nice game if you enjoy drawing. Draw two similar pictures but make six small adjustments on one of them. Then show them to your children and ask them if they can spot the six differences between the two pictures. For instance, draw a garden scene with different numbers of flowers or insects, with a sandpit with different toys and different shaped clouds in the sky.

Play tip
Make the differences more subtle for older children, e.g. the number of rays on the sun or petals on a flower.

Ferry crossing?
Pack a separate bag of essentials, including night things if it's an overnight trip, as you won't be able to return to your car once the ship is sailing. You won't necessarily need extra snack foods as there will be plenty on board.

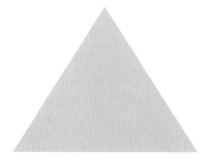

make a maze

age 4+
you'll need pencil and paper
suitable for boat, train, plane

Draw a treasure box in the centre of a piece of paper. Then put in the winning 'route' to the box by drawing a complicated set of bending pathways. Leave gaps in these pathways for false trails and add extra 'red herring' pathways to disguise the correct route. When it's complete, see if your child can trace his way to the treasure.

Play tip
You can use either straight lines or curvy ones for the route, which can be as long or short as your child's concentration allows.

shape pictures

age 4+
you'll need pencil, paper and coloured pencils or felt pens
suitable for boat, train, plane

Choose one shape and a theme, then get your children to draw pictures using only that shape, e.g. a person made from circles, a house made just from squares or a boat made just of triangles. When your children have finished their pictures they can count how many circles they have used and colour the pictures in.

Play tip
You could also buy a packet of gummed paper shapes and make more shape pictures with these.

animal faces

age 3+
you'll need pen and paper
suitable for boat, train, plane

Draw sets of four circles to represent four animal faces and ask your children to fill in the features. Try suitably shaped animals such as a pig, horse, cat, duck, dog, elephant and lion.

Play tip
You could also try rectangles, which will become four different types of vehicle, such as a bus, a lorry, a car or an ambulance.

complete the pattern

age 4+
you'll need pen and paper
suitable for boat, train, plane

This is a simple maths game. Create a simple pattern sequence such as a square, circle, triangle, square, circle, triangle, square, circle...Then ask your children if they can continue the sequence.

Play tip

Alternatively, fold some pieces of paper in half, draw a pattern on one half of each piece, stopping at the fold, and ask your children to complete the pattern on the other side of the paper. The pictures should end up looking symmetrical.

Nap time

A blow-up pillow can be very useful for toddlers wanting a nap. Choose a head-hugger-style pillow that can also be used in the car later.

whatever the weather

age 3+
you'll need pencil and paper
suitable for car, boat, train, plane

Draw a simple picture of a child wearing clothes suitable for a particular type of weather, e.g. a swim suit, scarf and hat, or boots and an umbrella. Ask her to add the right sort of weather to your picture, such as a big round sun, some snowflakes or raindrops.

Play tip

• Adapt this for the seasons by drawing two identical scenes (such as a park) and asking your child to add in the appropriate pictures for winter and summer, e.g.
• bare trees and trees with leaves
• ice on a pond and a boat on a pond
• children in coats and children in shorts.

CHAPTER 6

word games

GETTING IT RIGHT

Word games are great fun for school-age children, who'll enjoy the challenge of finding the right words to fit the game. Here are some points to remember:

- Pitch the game at a level suited to your children's abilities. If there's a young child with you, you may want to adapt the questions to make them suitable.

- If you know your children are very competitive, stick to games that don't pit them against each other.

- If a child doesn't immediately know the sound of a letter, say the letter name, and give a few examples of words that begin with that letter, e.g. 'the letter B sounds like "buh" – as in book, bun or bath'. This will help them to get started.

what's the opposite?

age 3+
You'll need nothing
Suitable for car, boat, train, plane

Simply ask your children to give you the opposite of each word you say. Good ones include:
- in and out
- big and small
- fat and thin
- under and over
- tall and short
- rough and smooth

Play tip

You could incorporate these opposites into a simple story, asking your children to fill in the gaps, e.g. 'The big bear climbed UP the hill, then he walked back DOWN again.'

- With some games you may need to check that the word is spelled correctly before the game begins, e.g. *Spell A Word*.

- Remember to give lots of praise. These games can be quite challenging and you want your children to feel successful, rather than unable to cope.

I packed my suitcase

age 4+
you'll need nothing
suitable for car, train, boat, plane

The object of this game is to remember as long a list as you can. Start by saying, 'I went to visit Grandma and in my suitcase I packed an apple.' The next person repeats the sentence and adds another item, this time beginning with 'B', such as 'balloon'. Continue like this as far along the alphabet as you are able to go.

Play tip
With a very young child you needn't bother to make the list alphabetical.

looney letters

age 5+
you'll need nothing
suitable for car

Take turns to choose a number plate from the cars that pass you and make a silly sentence from the blocks of letters. An example might be SAF Sheep Alarmed Frogs, or DBC Debbie Bought Caterpillars.

Play tip
Ban rude words or this game could quickly degenerate!

never say 'yes'

age 4+
you'll need nothing
suitable for car, train, boat, plane

In this game you must ask your opponent a series of questions and try to get them to answer either 'yes' or 'no'. If they slip up and say either of these words, they get a turn to try to catch you out. Questions might include:
- 'Is your name Ben?'
- 'Are you a girl?'
- 'Do you like sweets?'
- 'Do you go to school?'

Play tip
The trick with this game is to ask a yes/no question directly after a question that requires a longer answer, e.g. 'What colour is your bedroom painted? Is that your favourite colour?'

things that go together

age 4+
You'll need nothing
Suitable for car, boat, train, plane

Think of two objects that usually go together, such as a cup and saucer. Give your children the name of the first item and see if they can guess which thing should go with it. Other pairs to try include:

- knife and fork
- hat and coat
- brush and comb
- toothbrush and toothpaste
- socks and shoes.

Play tip
Adapt this game into word links, e.g. 'As kitten is to cat, puppy is to...?' or 'As calf is to cow, lamb is to....'

the doctor's dog

age 4+
you'll need nothing
suitable for car, train, boat, plane

The first person begins this descriptive alphabet game by saying, 'The doctor's dog was an *a*-mazing dog.' The next person adds another adjective that begins with '*b*', such as, 'The doctor's dog was a *b*-rainy dog,' and so on until the end of the alphabet.

Play tip
Make up some adventures about the extraordinary dog you've all described.

spell a word

age 5+
you'll need nothing
suitable for car

Ask each person in the car to choose a word with four letters. Then spot the letters, in order, on the number plates of passing cars. Make it clear that you can only have one letter from each number plate. Every time you see a correct letter, shout it out loud.

Play tip
You can make this game harder by choosing five, six or even seven-letter words.

give us another!

age 3+
you'll need nothing
suitable for car, train, boat, plane

Choose a category such as animals, fruit, colours or toys. Each player takes a turn to give an example of something within that category, such as teddy, doll, ball, bricks, etc if the category is toys. Carry on round the players until everyone has run out of ideas, then move to another category.

Play tip

For a more competitive version of this game, the person who can't think of another item in the category is out. Continue narrowing the field until there is only one player left, making them the winner.

word chain

age 5+
you'll need nothing
suitable for car, train, boat, plane

Start the game by thinking of a word, e.g. 'dog'. Find the last letter of that word – in this case 'g' – and the next player has to come up with a word beginning with 'g', such as 'goat'. Continue with the next player thinking of a word beginning with 't' and so on.

Play tip

To make it harder the words can all come from a single category such as animals or towns; to make it easier you can tell your child what the last letter of the word is, and sound it out for them.

Train travel

When travelling by train it's often worth booking your seats well ahead as you stand a much better chance of a good deal on the ticket price. Also ask for seats round a table if possible, so the children can draw or write during the journey.

bread, butter, knife

age 4+
you'll need nothing
suitable for car, train, boat, plane

The first player says a word like 'garden', then the next player says a word that either rhymes or is closely associated with it, such as 'grass'. The next player could say 'green'; the next 'red', and the next 'rose'. If anyone takes too long or repeats a word that's already been said, they are out.

Play tip
Nouns are usually the easiest words for starting this game.

Carry your own
Children will enjoy the responsibility of carrying their own rucksack with special treasures like toys and favourite books. This can also be useful once you're on holiday as you can pack each child's lunchbox, drink and beach kit in their rucksack so one adult doesn't end up laden with all the kids' gear.

mix up two words

age 6+
You'll need pencil and paper
Suitable for boat, train, plane

Think of two simple words such as cat and dog, or car and bus, and mix up all the letters. Ask your children to separate the letters out to make the two words again.

Play tip
Start with three-letter words and build up according to your children's abilities.

I went to the shops

age 6+
you'll need nothing
suitable for car, train, boat, plane

This is an alphabet game where each player takes a turn to say, 'I went to the shops and I bought a xxxx but I forgot my xxxx'. For example 'I went to the shops and I bought an Apple but I forgot my Atlas'. The next player's words begin with 'B' and so on.

Play tip
You can extend this game by adding a town or country name, e.g. 'I went to the shops in *Andover* and I bought ...'.

spot what's odd

age 3+
you'll need nothing
suitable for car, boat, train, plane

Ask your children if they can spot something wrong in the sentence you're going to say. Try things like:

- 'The ducks go woof woof.'
- 'Cows love to eat the tasty blue grass.'
- 'Your hair is long and green.'

Play tip
You could liven up this game by asking your children to make a specific noise when they hear the deliberate mistake, such as saying 'beep!' or 'rabbit!'

I like, I loathe

age 4+
you'll need nothing
suitable for car, train, boat, plane

This is a quick-fire game – too much dawdling and you're out! The first person names something they like, e.g. 'I like chips.' The next says something they don't like, e.g. 'I loathe spinach,' and so on until someone can't think of anything to say, and is out.

Play tip
You may find it easier to play this game in categories, such as fruit, vegetables, sports or insects.

60 seconds!

age 6+
you'll need a watch with a second hand
suitable for car, train, boat, plane

Select one player and ask them to speak on a subject of your choice for one minute. They mustn't hesitate, repeat themselves or go too far off the subject. If they do, they can be challenged by another player and that person has to continue the speech until the time is up – unless, of course, they in turn are interrupted. The person who is still speaking at the end of the minute is the winner.

Play tip
Be sure to choose a nice, easy subject that your children know something about and don't be too quick to cut them off.

I like lists!

age 4+
you'll need nothing
suitable for car, boat, train, plane

Start off a sentence saying, 'I am a boy who likes to play sport and I play with...' Your children then fill in the gap by listing all the equipment they can think of, for example, bat, ball, net, racket, swim suit, football boots, etc. Other categories could be:
• fruit
• cartoons
• types of toy

Play tip
Play this game with several children by giving them a point for each item they think of – the person with the most points wins.

Clean car
In the car, it's a good idea to keep a rubbish bag on the go for fruit peel, empty juice cartons and sweet wrappers. A plastic bag will do but change it frequently otherwise it'll soon get rather smelly!

name the parts
age 3+
you'll need nothing
suitable for car, boat, train, plane

Tell your children which object you're thinking of, e.g a bicycle. See how many parts of it they can name, e.g.
- saddle
- wheel
- chain
- gears
- handlebars
- brake
- bell

Other ideas include: a car, a train, a piano, a plant, a house or a tree.

Play tip
Older children may enjoy labelling a picture or diagram – either tear these out of a magazine or newspaper or ask them to draw their own.

story scramble
age 4+
you'll need nothing
suitable for car, boat, train, plane

Muddle up the events of a day and ask your children to put them in the right order. For instance, 'After my bath I went to bed. One morning I got up and ate my breakfast. At school I painted a picture. When I came home I watched TV. After breakfast I went to school.' Keep the sentences very short for young children.

Play tip
If your child can read confidently you could play this as a written game.

7

make and do games

GETTING IT RIGHT

You might think it's impossible to do any craft activities during a journey but if you stick to few basic items and a supply of paper, your children can create interesting bits and pieces while you're travelling. These tips will help make their creation a success:

- Take a small box packed with the basics – round-ended scissors, paper, a small roll of sticky tape, oddments of wool, a glue stick and colouring pencils and sharpener.

- If possible, settle down to do these activities at a table, which is possible on a train or coach, or possibly using the plane's meal tray. Unless your child is very self sufficient, these activities will be difficult to manage in a moving car.

- Have a rubbish bag ready so you don't scatter all the little bits everywhere.

paper fans
age 3+
you'll need large, rectangular piece of paper, sticky tape, crayons.
suitable for car, train, boat, plane

Fold the paper in a concertina style from one short side to the other. Then fold over the bottom of the fan, secure it with tape, and open out the top edge.

Play tip
Before securing bottom end, open out the fan and ask your child to decorate each section with a different pattern, using their crayons.

- You'll need to show your child how to make the craft items in this chapter, but once they've watched you they'll quickly learn how to make their own.

- If you know it's going to be a long trip, you could pre-prepare some of these activities.

- Take a plastic wallet or cardboard folder to store your child's creations.

- Keep it simple and don't get too ambitious: avoid glitter, paint or modelling clay.

threading cards
age 3+
you'll need thin card, hole punch, wool, sticky tape, pencil
suitable for car, train, boat, plane

Best prepared in advance, these simple activity cards are fun for even very young children. Draw a simple picture on the card, then punch holes at regular intervals around the edge of the picture. Wind sticky tape around the end of the wool to create a 'needle' (never use real needles), and show the children how to thread through the holes. Possible outlines could be a teddy, a boat, a star, a bird, a fish.

Play tip
Keep the cards small, the picture simple, and the outline close to the edge of the card so it's easy to reach with your hole punch.

lovely lanterns
age 3+
you'll need paper, scissors and sticky tape
suitable for car, train, boat

Fold a rectangular piece of paper in half so the two short sides meet. Make several cuts from the folded edge towards the open edge, leaving two or three centimetres uncut at the end. Then open out the sheet of paper, decorate the sections, join the vertical sides together with sticky tape or glue. Make a handle from a separate strip of paper. When it's finished, press the lantern down gently to give it a pleasing balloon shape.

Play tip
Use different sized sheets of paper to make a variety of lanterns.

doll concertinas

age 3+
you'll need paper, scissors, pencil, crayons
suitable for car, train, boat

Start with a long narrow strip of paper, and fold in a concertina style from one end to the other. Then draw a simple picture of a doll, cat, dog or anything you fancy on the top of the concertina, making sure at least some parts of the picture, ideally the hands and feet, touch the sides of the paper and are not cut through. Then cut around the outline, but avoid cutting through the places where the picture touches the sides. Unfold the concertina and admire the row of dancing dolls or clever cats. Your children can enjoy giving them all characteristics as they colour them in.

Play tip
It's essential that you don't cut through where the picture joins the sides or you'll end up with a pile of individual characters rather than a row. If you use stiff enough paper they'll stand up, too.

snowflakes

age 3+
you'll need paper, scissors
suitable for car, train, boat

Cut the paper into a circle, fold the paper in half, then in half again, and in half again, so you have a triangle shape. Use the scissors to make little snips in the three sides of the triangle, being careful to leave joins between each snip. Open out the snowflake to enjoy the beautiful pattern. Even the most haphazard of snips will make an unusual pattern. If you're really stuck, a paper napkin from the cafe will do to make a snowflake, and you can even tear the patterns with your fingers instead of using scissors.

Play tip
Once the snowflake is cut out, hold it securely over a separate piece of paper, and little ones will enjoy colouring through the holes like a stencil.

paper crowns
age 2+
you'll need paper, pencil, scissors, crayons
suitable for train, boat

For each child, fold a long strip of paper in a concertina style. Then simply cut one end into a pointed shape and open out. You will have a basis for crowns which your children can colour in. When they have finished join the ends together with some sticky tape and put in on their heads. If the paper is not long enough to go round their heads, make two and stick them together.

Play tip
Vary the shapes you cut out along the top to vary the effect. Try crennellations (where you cut in squares) or adding a bobble to your point for 'jewels'.

spirals
age 3+
you'll need paper, pencil, scissors, crayons
suitable for car, train, boat

Mark a spot at the centre of the paper with a pencil, and draw out in ever increasing circles to form a spiral. When you reach the edge of the paper, stop and cut back carefully along your line until you reach the dot in the centre again. Then hold up the middle and let your 3-D spiral dangle down. Your child can decorate it at this stage, or could make it into a snake by adding a face to one end.

Play tip
This works best if you start with a square piece of paper as your spiral will be more even.

Plane comfort
If you've got a young baby and you're booking seats on a plane, ask for bulkhead seats if possible to give you some more leg room. If this isn't possible, ask if you can have an aisle seat, so that you can get out easily.

colour your hands
age 2+
you'll need paper, pencil, crayon
suitable for car, train, boat, plane

Draw round each of your children's hands. Then they can colour them in the outlines, adding rings and decorations.

Play tip
Your children may be able to draw round their own hands, or enjoy drawing round yours too.

pom-pom
age 3+
you'll need identical circles of card with an inner circle cut out of each, a ball of wool and some scissors
suitable for car, boat, train

For each pom-pom, hold two circles of card together, and start winding the wool round and round the card until the hole in the centre is almost closed up. Snip around the outside of the circle, separate the two cards and tie a piece of wool tightly around the middle. Then gently remove the two pieces of card and fluff up the pom-pom.

Play tip
When tying the centre of the pom-pom, allow an extra length of wool so your child can hold and dangle it.

paper tree
age 3+
you'll need paper and sticky tape, scissors
suitable for car, train, boat

Take a long strip of paper (newspaper is ideal, but messy) and roll it loosely from one short side to the other. Make several snips down to the middle. Fan out the strips, then very carefully pull on a section from the centre to create a splendid bushy tree. Secure the 'trunk' with sticky tape.

Play tip
Don't pull the tree too far or it will fall apart.

Buggy know-how
To make life easier, ask if you can take your lightweight buggy right up to the aircraft. You'll have to hand it over when you board but it will be ready for you as soon as you disembark.

picture lotto

age 3+
you'll need paper, crayons, scissors
suitable for train, boat

Draw several pairs of pictures in cards and cut them out. Give one set to your child, and then put yours out randomly one at a time and see if she can find the right one to put on top. You can play with more than one child, but you'll need to make extra cards.

Play tip
Your child may enjoy colouring in the cards before you play.

plaiting

age 6+
you'll need wool, already cut to length
suitable for car, train, boat, plane

Cut three lengths of wool for each child and tie them together in a knot at the top. Then show the children how to plait a long 'rope' by weaving the three strands together by laying them left over middle, right over middle, left over middle, right over middle and so on.

Play tip
Use three different colours of wool to make a more vibrant plait.

paper boats
age 3+
you'll need rectangular pieces of paper, crayons
suitable for car, train, boat, plane

Make a boat for each child in the following way. Fold the paper in half vertically. Then turn it with the folded edge uppermost. Fold down the top two corners so they meet in the middle. Then fold up the bottom parts of the paper on either side, to create a boat – or hat!

Play tip
Pretend it's Noah's Ark and ask your child to draw animals around the edge of the boat.

my shop
age 3+
you'll need paper, crayons
suitable for car, train, boat, plane

This very simple game simply involves folding a rectangular piece of paper for each child so that the two sides meet in the middle to form 'doors' to the shop. Open the doors and draw 'shelves' and the children can then draw their own things for the shops, such as food, toys or cups and plates.

Play tip
Your children may want to decorate the doors to their shops, too, with shop signs over the top. With luck, your shop will stand up.

walk-through circle

age 4+
you'll need paper, scissors
suitable for boat

Fold a piece of paper in half. Then make narrow alternate cuts from either side to about 1cm from the edge (do not cut right through). Finish off by snipping carefully directly along the fold, avoiding the two end sections. Gently open out your piece of paper and you should have a circle that you can step through.

Play tip

For an impressive party trick, try this with a postcard. Open by holding up the postcard and saying, 'Bet you don't believe I can step through this postcard!', then make as many narrow slits as you can.

Baby change

Remember to change your baby's nappy just before you get on to a train. Although many trains have a drop-down changing surface in the toilet, it's very cramped – and often busy!

wool bracelets

age 3+
you'll need strips of card, sticky tape and some wool that you have already cut into lengths
suitable for car, boat, train, plane

For each bracelet, join the ends of a strip of card with sticky tape to make a ring that fits over each child's hand. Then stick down the end of a piece of wool on to the inside of each ring and ask your children to wind the wool over and over so that it covers the ring completely to make a pretty wool bracelet.

Play tip

Use shorter lengths of wool for younger children so that they don't get in too much of a tangle.

squaring up

age 5+

you'll need paper and pencil

suitable for boat, train, plane

For each child, draw a picture of an object, such as a vase of flowers, then draw a grid of squares over it. Repeat the grid just below your picture and ask your children to copy the picture square by square.

Play tip

Use smaller or larger squares depending on how complicated your picture is.

going dotty

age 2+

you'll need paper and a packet of stick-on dots

suitable for boat, train, plane

Stick-on dots have a tremendous fascination for little children. Show your children how to stick them onto paper to make a smiley face, a flower, a long wiggly snake or a simple colour pattern.

Play tip

Stick some onto their nails for instant 'nail polish'.

pretty fingers!

age 2+

you'll need Some small strips of card, sticky tape and a few stick-on dots or shapes

suitable for boat, train, plane

Make a collection of card rings to fit your children's fingers and then let them decorate these with the stick-on dots and shapes. Decorate them with felt pens instead of dots or shapes if you prefer.

Play tip

If your children find the rings a bit fiddly, let them decorate the strips of card before you make them into rings.

flap house
age 4+
you'll need paper, pencils, crayons, scissors, sticky tape
suitable for boat, train

Draw a simple picture of a house and make a 'doorway' by cutting round three sides of a rectangle. Stick the house, but not the door, on to a second piece of paper, open the door and ask your child to draw herself underneath.

Play tip
If your child is very competent at this, you could make flap windows as well and draw a cat, plant, teddy and flowers in the other rooms of the house.

paper feathers
age 3+
you'll need paper, scissors and coloured pencils or felt pens
suitable for car, boat, train

Fold pieces of paper in half lengthways and cut out rough feather shapes. Then get your children to snip a few feathery cuts from the outside edge towards the fold (being very careful not to cut through the fold). They can then open the feathers out and decorate them.

Play tip
Make several paper feathers of different sizes and stick them onto card strips to make simple head-dresses.

CHAPTER **8**

hand and finger games

GETTING IT RIGHT

A few hand and finger games can be invaluable for filling in moments when you're on a long train or boat journey, or are having to wait around at airports.

- Little children often can't quite manage all the actions but will still enjoy joining in. Don't worry if they get things wrong, it's the playing that counts.

- Some games have complicated actions, but you can simplify them to suit your children's level of ability.

- Encourage older children to play their part in entertaining the little ones on a long journey. They'll like having an excuse to play rhymes and games that they enjoyed when they were younger.

- If your child is very keen on thumb or finger sucking, don't draw faces on those particular fingers.

fingertip people

age 2+
you'll need one or two felt-tip pens
suitable for car, boat, train, plane

Using a felt-tip pen, draw a little face on the tip of one of your child's fingers so she can wiggle it about and make it 'talk'. If this goes down well you can draw on a second finger, and so on. Encourage her to make up stories about the people. Alternatively you can draw the people on your own fingers if your child isn't keen on having her fingers coloured!

Play tip

Draw characters for a specific tale such as the 'Three Little Pigs', for example, so your child can act out the story with her fingertip people as you tell the tale.

- If your child's unhappy about having finger people washed off, pretend they are having a bath!

- Don't forget clapping games. Little children will enjoy simply clapping out their birthday number or singing along to *If You're Happy and You Know It, Clap Your Hands*.

hand monster

age 3+
you'll need a felt-tip pen
suitable for car, boat, train, plane

Ask your children to hold their hands out so their thumbs are lying flush against their first fingers. When they moves their thumbs it should look like mouths opening and closing. Draw the 'lips' around the mouth area and draw on eyes and noses to finish the monsters.

Play tip
Sing a song and see if your children can make the monsters' mouths move, so it looks as though they're singing along too.

two little dicky-birds

age 2+
you'll need nothing
suitable for car, boat, train, plane

An old favourite that still delights new generations of children. Hold up your two index fingers (one is Peter, the other Paul) and make them wiggle as if sitting on a wall. Then fly each one away separately by putting your hand behind your back for the third line, and bring back first Peter and then Paul for the fourth line.

> *Two little dicky-birds,*
> *sitting on a wall*
> *One named Peter,*
> *one named Paul.*
> *Fly away Peter, fly away Paul,*
> *Come back Peter,*
> *come back Paul.*

Play tip
Put different coloured sticky dots on each finger to help your child distinguish between Peter and Paul – or draw a small coloured dot on each finger with a felt-tip pen.

scissors, stone, paper

age 5+
you'll need nothing
suitable for car, train, boat, plane

This game is for two players. You need to show the children three basic movements for scissors, stone and paper. For scissors, use your first two fingers to make snipping 'scissors'; for stone, make a fist; for paper, hold out a flat hand. To play the game, each hold out a fist and count 'one, two, three.' On the 'three' each of you turns your hand into stone, scissors or paper. Paper wins over stone because it can wrap it, but loses to scissors that can cut it. Stone wins over scissors because it can blunt them, but loses to paper. Scissors win over paper, but loses to stone.

ten in the bed

age 3+
you'll need nothing
suitable for car, train, boat, plane

This is a fun action and counting game. Hold up the correct number of fingers for each verse – losing one each time – and roll your arms round and round each other as you sing the rolling parts of each verse. When you get to 'and one fell out', drop your hands down in front of you.

There were ten in the bed
And the little one said,
'Roll over, roll over!'
So they all rolled over
and one fell out.
There were nine in the bed ...

Play tip
Younger children won't be able to hold up the right numbers of fingers, so do this bit for them.

my lady's table
age 3+
you'll need nothing
suitable for car, train, boat, plane

This is a finger game. With your hands back to back, link your fingers together and wiggle them for 'knives and forks'. Turn your hands over to make a flat 'table', then lift your index fingers to create an arch for the 'looking glass'. Finally raise your little fingers too to make a cradle shape which you can rock from side to side.

Here are my lady's knives and forks,
Here's my lady's table.
Here's my lady's looking-glass
And here's her baby's cradle!

Play tip
If you can't remember all the actions for this, just improvise your own.

Don't get dehydrated
Travelling is thirsty work. Always have a bottle of water with you, especially in the car when it can be a while before you reach the next service station. Don't drink while driving, though. Children often like sports bottles of water, though stick to a spill-proof beaker for toddlers.

wind the bobbin up
age 3+
you'll need nothing
suitable for car, train, boat, plane

A playgroup favourite, this translates well to confined spaces. Start by rolling your fists round each other for winding the bobbin, next link your fingers and gently pull, then clap three times. The other actions speak for themselves.

Wind the bobbin up,
Wind the bobbin up.
Pull, pull, clap, clap, clap.
Point to the ceiling,
point to the floor.
Point to the window,
point to the door.
Clap your hands together,
one, two, three.
Put your hands upon your knee.

Play tip
If you don't know the tune for this, ask older children – the chances are that they'll have learned it at a playgroup.

spider takes a walk

age 2+
you'll need nothing
suitable for car, train, boat, plane

A simple game for babies and toddlers. Simply pretend one of your hands is a friendly spider and name all the body parts as he slowly walks around your child's body. The spider's walk ends with a loving tickle.

Play tip
If your child doesn't like spiders, turn the 'person' walking into a teddy.

which hand?

age 2+
you'll need A little toy or small object
suitable for car, train, boat, plane

Hide the object in one fist and hold out both. Ask your child to guess which hand is hiding the toy. This game is surprisingly popular and will probably last as long as you want it to.

Play tip
Let your child have a go at hiding the object – but make sure it's not small enough to be a choking hazard.

two fat gentlemen

age 3+
you'll need nothing
suitable for car, train, boat, plane

Hold up your two index fingers to be the gentlemen facing each other. Make them 'bow' one at a time, except on the last line when they bow together.

Two fat gentlemen
met in a lane.
Bowed most politely,
bowed once again.
'How do you do?'
'How do you do?'

And 'How do you do?' again.

Play tip
After the gentlemen you can make up your own characters to meet in the lane and do funny voices for them. Try the following:
- **Two smart ladies**
- **Two tall policemen**
- **Two naughty schoolboys**
- **Two little babies for your little fingers**

five little ducks

age 2+
you'll need nothing
suitable for car, train, boat, plane

Hold up five fingers and wriggle them to make them 'swim'. Next make a wavy movement with your arm to suggest the hills, and use your thumb and fingers to make a quacking beak shape. Finally hold up fingers to represent the returning ducks. Continue until all the little ducks have swum away, then change the last line of the final verse to say, 'And all five ducks came swimming right back.'

Five little ducks went swimming one day,
Over the hills and far away.
Mummy Duck said, 'Quack, quack, quack, quack!'
But only four little ducks came back.

Play tip

If your child really loves this song, start with ten ducks to make it last longer.

there was a little mouse

age 1+
you'll need nothing
suitable for car, boat, train, plane

Run your finger gently round your child's palm as you say this rhyme:

There was a little mouse
And he lived right there (point to middle of palm)
But if anybody saw him (pause)
He ran tickly under there! (run fingers up her arm and tickle under it)

Play tip

The other classic tickling game is 'Round and round the garden, like a teddy bear, one step, two step... tickly under there!'

Toilet breaks

Allow plenty of chances for toilet stops on a long journey. Even if you think it wasn't long ago since everyone stopped, there's nearly always someone who does want to go. A good motto is 'When there's a toilet, use it!'

five fat peas

age 3+
you'll need nothing
suitable for car, boat, train, plane

Sing the song below, following the suggested finger actions and get your children to copy you.

Five fat peas in a pea-pod pressed
(Press the palms of your hands together)
One grew, two grew, and so did all the rest.
(Gradually move the palms of your hands apart)
They grew and they grew and they did not stop,
(Continue moving hands apart until your arms are extended)
Until one day the pod went pop!
(Bring your hands together in a loud clap)

Play tip
To change this favourite rhyme, substitute seeds or beans for peas.

the grand old Duke of York

age 2+
you'll need nothing
suitable for boat, train

Sing the nursery rhyme below, following the suggested actions.

Oh, the grand old Duke of York,
(Salute with your hand)
He had 10,000 men.
(Wave your fingers in the air)
He marched them up to the top of the hill,
(March your fingers up the hill)
Then he marched them down again.
(March your fingers down)

Play tip
Try substituting your town for 'the grand old Duke of York', e.g. 'Oh the grand young boy of Leeds'.

Hot baby
Remember in very warm weather your baby will need extra breastfeeds or cooled boiled water if you're bottlefeeding.

Grandma's spectacles

age 2+
you'll need nothing
suitable for car, boat, train, plane

Sing the song below, following the suggested actions and get your children to copy you.

Here are Grandma's spectacles
(Make small rings with fingers and put them over your eyes)
Here is Grandma's hat.
(Make a small hat with hands and put it on your head)
This is the way she folds her hands
(Fold your hands)
And puts them in her lap.
(Lay them in your lap)

Here are Grandad's spectacles
(Make big rings with fingers and put them over your eyes)
Here is Grandad's hat.
(Make a big hat with hands and put it on your head)
This is the way he folds his arms
(Fold your arms)
And takes a little nap.
(Close your eyes and pretend to snore)

Play tip
Substitute other members of the family to make this game more personal.

pray open your umbrella

age 2+
you'll need nothing
suitable for car, boat, train, plane

This simple song with actions can be enjoyed by even very little children, who can copy you.

Pray open your umbrella (move arms up slightly)
Pray open your umbrella (move them up a little higher)
Pray open your umbrella (hands meet over your head)
To shield me from the rain.

The rain is nearly over (gradually lower arms)
The rain is nearly over
The rain is nearly over
So close it down again (finally lower them down)

Play tip
If your children enjoy this, play it again with the umbrella shielding them from the snow, the hail, the wind, etc.

ten fat sausages

age 4+
you'll need nothing
suitable for car, boat, train, plane

This is a fun counting-down song with actions, which your children can copy, to match.

Ten fat sausages
(Wiggle all ten fingers)
Sizzling in the pan.
One went pop!
(Clap)
And another went bang!
(Clap)

For subsequent verses start with eight, six, four and two sausages (and fingers). The final verse is:

No fat sausages
(Hold out your empty palms)
Sizzling in the pan.
None to go pop!
(clap)
And none to go bang!
(clap)

Play tip
Talk about the other foods you would eat with sausages.

five little speckled frogs

age 3+
you'll need nothing
suitable for car, boat, train, plane

Sing the song below, following the suggested actions.

Five little freckled frogs
(Hold up five fingers)
Sat on a speckled log,
(Rest one hand on the other)
Eating a most delicious grub –
yum yum!
(Make your fingers into a mouth shape)

One jumped into the pool,
(Dive one hand over the other)
Where it was nice and cool,
(Swim one hand along)
Then there were four freckled
frogs – glub, glub!
(Hold up four fingers now)

Repeat the song until there are no freckled frogs left.

Play tip
You could draw some froggy faces on your children's fingertips.

this little piggy

age 1+
you'll need nothing
suitable for car, boat, train, plane

Play this classic game with fingers or toes, holding one for each verse, and tickling your child's foot or palm at the end of the rhyme.

> *This little piggy went to market,*
> *This little piggy stayed at home.*
> *This little piggy had roast beef,*
> *And this piggy had none.*
> *And this little piggy cried,*
> *'Wee, wee, wee! I can't find my way home!'*

Play tip
Vary the game by substituting a different animal each time, such as pony, cat, puppy or duck, with the appropriate animal noise for the last line, e.g. 'Quack, quack, quack, I can't find my way home!'

here's the church

age 4+
you'll need nothing
suitable for car, boat, train, plane

This simple finger game is always popular with little ones.

> *Here's the church*
> (Lace your hands together so your fingers face in towards your palms with your thumbs side by side as the doors.)
> *Here's the steeple*
> (Raise your two index fingers in an arch)
> *Open the doors*
> (Move your thumbs apart)
> *Here are all the people!*
> (Wiggle your fingers)

Play tip
Your children will need a fair degree of coordination to do this themselves – if it's too hard you can show them your hands.

imaginative games

GETTING IT RIGHT

A good imaginative game can last for ages but there are a few things to bear in mind:

- Little children often need a bit of prompting to get started. If your child is stuck, offer him some options that he can choose from.

- Many of the games here can be extended by drawing pictures of the things you've invented or described. On a plane you can let down the food tray to draw on.

- Don't forget to take a couple of your child's favourite story books as these can often be the starting point for a new imaginary game.

- Tired young children will enjoy sitting on your lap while you simply give a running commentary about all the things going on outside the window.

story circle

age 4+
you'll need nothing
suitable for car, train, boat, plane

Begin the game by starting a story with a tempting opening line, such as, 'Once upon a time there was a little princess who had lost her shoes,' or 'There was once a pirate who was afraid of water.' Then ask each child to add the next part of story in turn and when they run out of steam you take over again.

Play tip

If you can't think of a story, tell a traditional tale, that you all know, in your own words.

- Don't expect hungry or thirsty children to be interested in playing a game.

- Imaginary games can be quite demanding, so switch to another activity if you feel your child is becoming bored or tired.

teddy's picnic
age 2+
you'll need nothing
suitable for car, train, boat, plane

A game for tinies where you say their teddy (doll or other soft toy) is going on a picnic in the woods with all his friends. Together you decide what lovely foods they'll pack in their picnic basket and games they'll play when they've had their tea.

Play tip
If you've brought some little snacks with you set them out and pretend that's the picnic.

what would you do?
age 4+
you'll need nothing
suitable for car, train, boat, plan

Give your children a dramatic scenario to imagine, such as 'You're stuck up a tree with a short rope, a torch and a sandwich. Two hungry lions are circling round the tree. Night is falling, what do you do?' Your children have to come with an escape plan using only the props you've suggested.

Play tip
Other scenes you could try include: under the sea with a shark; locked in a tall tower by a witch; lost in a desert with snakes all around; and on an ice floe with a polar bear closing in.

on holiday
age 4+
you'll need nothing
suitable for car, boat, train, plane

An easy one, this. Just take it in turns to describe your ideal holiday. Details to include are location, weather, activities, food, and clothes.

Play tip
Use this as a springboard to discuss everyone's memories of your last family holiday.

my sort of place
age 3+
you'll need nothing
suitable for car, train, boat, plane

This game enables your children to create a whole imaginary world in their heads. Tell them that they are astronauts in a rocket that is just coming to land on a brand new planet. They get out of their rocket and are the very first people ever to look round. Encourage them to start describing it.

- What does the planet look like?
- Does it have a name?
- Are there any animals or aliens on it?
- Where will they build their camp?

Play tip
Other scenarios you could try might include a secret garden, an underwater palace, or a wonderful fun fair.

funny animals
age 5+
you'll need nothing
suitable for car, train, boat, plane

Think of two different animals that you could put together to make a totally new creature. For example a zebraphant (zebra and elephant), a girocodile (giraffe and crocodile) or a caterfrog (caterpiller and frog).

Play tip
Start with animals that are similar in size but once your children get the hang of the game experiment with animals of different sizes, such as a butterfly and a hippo.

play people

age 2+
you'll need A few small play figures or animals
suitable for car, train, boat, plane

Simple but usually very effective. Have a couple of play figures in your bag and take them out when the whining starts. Help your children to start a game with them by suggesting what they might be doing, such as mountaineering up the window or galloping across your lap.

Play tip
Make sure you are not using older children's play figures for under-threes.

cloud shapes

age 3+
you'll need a cloudy day
suitable for car, boat, train

An old favourite. Just look up at the clouds and ask your children to see what shapes they think the clouds could be. If they need a bit of help getting started, try suggesting such things as a castle, a dragon, a bear, a bird or a boat.

Play tip
Make sure none of you ever looks directly at the sun as it could damage your eyes.

create a character

age 3+
you'll need nothing
suitable for car, train, boat, plane

This is a form of *Consequences* where each person has to describe a new bit to make an imaginary character. You'll need head, eyes, ears, body, arms, legs and feet – and a name if you want. For instance one person thinks of a big purple head, the next suggests green googly eyes, the next big pink ears, and so on.

Play tip
You could choose a theme to create your character around, such as a clown, alien, ballerina or robot.

Potty know-how
Even if your younger children are toilet trained, take a travel potty along with you.

talking on the phone

age 3+
you'll need nothing
suitable for car, boat, train, plane

Even very little children like to have pretend conversations. Start the game by making noises like a ringing telephone and holding your hand up to your ear as a pretend mobile phone. Then say in a special voice, 'Hello, is that Jo? Oh I'm so glad it is, because I've been asked to tell him that a spaceship has just landed in his garden. Have you ever been in a spaceship, Jo? Can you tell me what it was like?'

Play tip
Pretend to be particular characters, such as a garage mechanic who's finished mending your child's car; a pop group who wants your child to choose a song for them; or a teacher who's looking for some new subjects to teach at school.

Stay cool
In the car, always make sure your children are well shaded from the sun – use window blinds on side windows.

race-track

age 2+
you'll need a few toy cars, a piece of paper and a pen
suitable for car, train, boat, plane

Draw a simple race-track on paper, with some twists and turns to add interest. Let your child drive a toy car around the race track, staying inside the lines. You could pretend to have a race if you join in with another car.

Play tip
Add some extras to the scene like a garage, a shop and a bridge for the car to stop at or drive over.

take three

age 4+
you'll need nothing
suitable for car, boat, train, plane

One person has to think of three objects for the other to make up a story about. You can make these as easy or hard as you like. Easy ones could be a knight, a dragon, and a horde of jewels; a harder selection could be a spy, a detective and a suitcase.

Play tip
Let each child have a chance to think of the three objects so that you have to tell the story.

if only they could talk ...

age 3+
you'll need nothing
suitable for car, train, boat, plane

Think of an animal and ask each child what he thinks it might say if it could talk. For example, a bird singing at the top of a tree; a snail crawling up to a juicy leaf; a chicken scratching in the farmyard or even your own family pet, if you have one.

Play tip
Look out for animals that you can see on your journey, such as cows and sheep in fields.

three wishes

age 4+
you'll need nothing
suitable for car, boat, train, plane

Many fairy stories allow the main character to have three wishes. If your child was given this chance what wishes would he choose and why?

Play tip
Set a few rules for this game, such as you can't wish for anything bad to happen to anyone, or to wish for more wishes.

who would win?

age 4+
you'll need nothing
suitable for car, boat, train, plane

A favourite with boys, this game simply involves lining up two opposing sides with different characteristics and skills. The object is to describe who would win, and why. For example, if six elephants with big tusks and ten lions with sharp teeth both wanted to be first to the water hole, who would win?

Play tip
If this is too aggressive, you could set up a game scenario such as three monkeys playing basketball with two bears, who would win? (The bears are taller, but the monkeys could climb up the posts.)

the grandest party in the world!

age 4+
you'll need nothing
suitable for car, boat, train, plane

It's your child's birthday and you're going to throw him the grandest party in the world.
- Where would he like it to be?
- What would the room look like?
- What would the guests wear?
- What would they have to eat?
- What would the cake be like?
- What games would you play?
- What going-home presents would you give your guests?

The bigger and more extravagant the ideas the better!

Play tip
Describe parties for different celebrations, such as for Christmas or for a new baby, or for groups of people who like specific things, such as sports cars, films, music or outdoor activities.

my ideal house

age 4+
you'll need nothing
suitable for car, boat, train, plane

If money was no object, what sort of house and garden would your children like to live in? What would their bedrooms be like? Would they have:
- a toy room
- a swimming pool
- a library of books
- a garden full of trees to climb
- a field for horses

Play tip
When your child finishes describing his ideal house, ask him where it would be, and why.

perfect presents

age 4+
you'll need nothing
suitable for car, boat, train, plane

Most children love to think about what toys they want for their birthday or Christmas. But what if there weren't any toyshops – what would they like then?

Play tip
This can be quite difficult, so your child might need a bit of prompting to get started. Try suggesting things you might like, such as a big bunch of flowers, all the washing-up to be done by magic, a sunny day, or even a large kiss.

what's your favourite?

age 2+
you'll need nothing
suitable for car, boat, train, plane

Choose a category and ask all the people in your family to say what their favourite thing within this category would be. Good categories could include:
● books
● films
● sweets and meals
● toys, games and sports

Play tip
You could also play this by saying what your worst thing would be!

what would you wear?

age 4+
you'll need nothing
suitable for car, boat, train, plane

Describe a situation and ask your children to think what they might wear if they found themselves in that situation. For instance you could suggest being:
● at the bottom of the ocean
● on the top of a mountain
● at a fancy dress ball
● in an old-fashioned open-topped car
● in the desert or jungle
● at a party of pop stars

Play tip
Try bringing the seasons into this game, so that your child might be on a beach in winter, or a boat in summer.

journey extras

When you're on a long journey there are a few extra supplies that can really save the day. It's worth buying and packing these well in advance, especially with books and activities for your children where you'll have the benefit of surprise on your side when you eventually produce them.

personal cassette player

This is probably one of the easiest ways to keep children entertained on a long journey. From around three, your child will enjoy listening to a story or song tape on his own cassette player. Take a few favourite tapes and add a couple of new ones (libraries usually have a good stock to choose from). For older children you can buy an adapter that means they can both listen to the same tape on their headphones and so enjoy the story together. Always check the volume isn't too high.

Toys

You probably don't want to take masses of toys but useful games and activities to consider include travel versions of board games, dominoes, a felt shape set, a magnetic shape board, paper dolls and finger puppets.

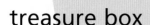

sticker books and other activities

treasure box

This can simply be a cardboard shoe box filled with a few interesting novelties (party bits and pieces are ideal). Things to try could include: mini puzzles; old-fashioned pegs to make into dolls; a notebook and pencil; mini magic sketchboard and mini jigsaws. Even some interesting old postcards or toy catalogues can be fun to look at.

Ever popular, these are a handy standby, especially if they have reusable stickers. Look out for make-a-scene sets, too, where your child sticks transfers onto a basic background scene, such as a garage, farm or jungle.

Other practical 'treats' include dot-to-dot books, puzzle books, colouring books, geometric pattern pads and of course the essential pad of paper, pencils and crayons (a new exercise book with plain pages is popular with most children). Felt-tip pens are best kept for older children who are less likely to scribble on themselves or on the surrounding seats.

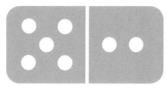

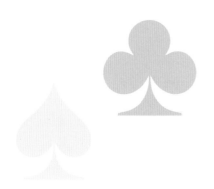

cards

A pack of cards takes very little room but has lots of play potential, even for very young children. Buy a cheap pack so that it doesn't matter whether they get lost or damaged. Here are some simple activities and easy games you can play together.

Clean up time

Some wet wipes or a clean damp flannel in a plastic bag is invaluable for wiping faces, washing sticky fingers or simply freshening up when the going gets hot. Look out for travel packs of wipes that you can pop in your bag or the glove compartment. If it's a flannel, remember to wash it out thoroughly on arrival so that it's clean for the return journey.

find the suit (age 4+)
Shuffle the pack well, then ask your child to sort the cards into the four suits. If she's able, she could also put each suit in numerical order.

pairs (age 5+)
Turn all the cards face down. Turn over two at a time. If they are a pair you can keep them, and have another turn. If they're not a pair, turn them back over, and the other person has their go. Continue until all the pairs are found. Make it easier by limiting the number of pairs you set out in the first place.

snap (age 5+)
Deal out all the cards between you. Put them face down in front of you, and take turns to turn over the top card of your pile, putting it in the centre. If you turn over a card that's the same as the one the other person has just put out, shout, 'SNAP!' and take the pile of cards. Put them underneath your pile, and continue until someone has won all the cards.

You can buy a pack of picture snap cards for younger children, as playing with an ordinary pack is only suitable for children who know their numbers well.

pick up the pack (age 6+)

Divide the pack in half. Turn over alternate cards into a pile in the middle. If you put down a Jack, your opponent has to pay you one card by adding it to the pile in the middle, and you get to keep the pile. If you put down a Queen, your opponent pays two cards; if you put down a King, it's three cards, and four cards for an Ace. The fun starts if your opponent puts down a Court Card while 'paying' you – because *you* then have to put down cards to pay *them*. The winner is the first to take all the cards.

sevens (age 6+)

Deal the cards between you. Whoever has the seven of Hearts puts it out in the middle. If the next player has the six or eight of hearts, they can put this out, either above or below the seven. Alternatively, if they have a seven of another suit, they can put this out beside the seven of hearts. Each player has to try to build either up or down the four columns so that eventually all the cards are laid out in columns with the sevens in the middle. If you don't have a card that can be placed, you knock on the table and miss a go. The object of the game is to be the first to get rid of all your cards.

CHAPTER 11

games
by age

To help you choose games that are suitable for your journey, we have given each of them a minimum age, but of course older children will enjoy playing them too. It may help to jot down a suitable selection and mark these pages with sticky notes before you set off.

AGE 1+

AGE 2+

AGE 5+

AGE 6+

index

Acknowledgments

Executive Editor **Jane McIntosh**
Editor **Rachel Lawrence**
Executive Art Editor **Rozelle Bentheim**
Designer **Emily Wilkinson**
Production Controller **Ian Paton**
Illustrations by Emily Wilkinson
Index compiled by Indexing Specialists